NOTE TO PARENTS

This familiar Bible story has been retold in a sensitive and simple way so that young children can read and understand it for themselves. But the special message of the story remains unchanged. It is the message of God's love and care for us all.

David and Goliath

retold by Marjorie Newman
illustrated by Edgar Hodges

Copyright © 1990 World International Publishing Ltd.
All rights reserved.
Published in Great Britain by World International Publishing Ltd.,
an Egmont Company, Egmont House, PO Box 111, Great Ducie Street,
Manchester M60 3BL.
Printed in Germany.
ISBN 0 7235 4467 0
Reprinted 1992

A catalogue record for this book is available from the British Library

Once there was a shepherd boy called David. He looked after his father's sheep. It wasn't an easy job!

Every day, David had to lead the sheep to fresh grass and cool water. While they grazed, he sang to them. But fresh grass was hard to find. And David had to watch out for bears and lions!

Sometimes David had to lead the sheep through
a deep, dark, dangerous valley. One day as they
went along, David saw a lion! It was trying to carry
off a lamb! "Baa! Baa!" bleated the lamb, in fear.

David could have run away. But he cared about the sheep. And he loved and trusted God. Quickly he prayed, "Please, God, make me brave and strong!" And he fought off the lion. Another day he fought off a bear!

David always wanted to tell his father Jesse about his adventures. But one day everyone at home was too excited to listen. The armies of the Philistines had marched into the land of the Israelites. There was to be a battle!

Jesse was too old to join King Saul's army. But David's three big brothers set off to join. "We Israelites will soon get rid of these Philistines!" they cried.

David sighed. He wished he could have gone, too. But he had to stay with the sheep.

Time went by. No news came. Jesse began to worry. Could King Saul's army have been beaten? "David," said Jesse, "take this food to your brothers. The cheeses are a present for their captain. Find out what is happening."

David left a shepherd in charge of the sheep. Then, happily, he set out. It was a long walk. At last he saw the tents of King Saul's army.

He reached the camp. The soldiers were being ordered to their places! Excitedly, David left the food with the keeper of the supplies and ran to find his brothers.

Suddenly a huge voice echoed across the valley. "Ho, Israelites! I dare one of you to fight me! If he kills me, you win the battle. But if *I* kill *him*, *we* win!" It was the giant, Goliath.

David waited for an Israelite to step forward. But they all ran back to their tents!

"The King has offered a rich reward for anyone who will fight Goliath," said David's brothers, trembling. "But he is too strong!"

"I will fight him," said David. "*You*!" cried his brothers. "You're showing off! Go back to your sheep!"

But some of the soldiers heard what David had said. They went to tell King Saul.

Saul sent for David. "You are only a boy!" cried the king. "You cannot fight a giant!"

"God helped me when I fought a lion and a bear," said David. "He will help me now."

"Then go, and God be with you," said King Saul.

The king put his own armour on David. Clank! Clank!

David tried to move. "This armour is too heavy for me!" he said. "Please take it off! I will use only my shepherd's sling."

David went down to the brook which ran through the valley. Carefully, he chose five small round stones. He put them into his shepherd's bag.

Goliath came striding out of the Philistines' camp.
Then he saw David. "What!" he roared. "A young
lad dares to fight me? And am I a dog, that you
come with a stick? I shall feed you to the birds!"

Bravely David faced Goliath. "You have your armour!" he shouted across the valley. "But God is with me! And He will let me win this fight, so that everyone may know He is the true God!"

With an angry roar, Goliath began to charge down the hill towards David.

Swiftly, David placed a stone in his sling. He whirled the sling round and round. Then he let the stone fly. The stone flew straight to the giant's forehead. And Goliath fell down dead.

The Philistines saw what had happened. They turned and ran. With a great cheer, the Israelites ran after them. They chased the Philistines right out of their country.

King Saul was very pleased with David. David was invited to live at the palace. Sometimes he played his harp for the king. Sometimes he fought in the king's army. But never again did he have to look after his father's sheep.